DiscipleHelps

SPIRITUAL JOURNAL FOR STUDENTS

THIS JOURNAL BELONGS TO

_____

BEGINNING DATE

_____

SUBJECT

_____

LIFEWAY PRESS®
NASHVILLE, TENNESSEE

ISBN: 978-0-6331-9381-2
Item 001244528

Dewey Decimal Classification Number: 220.07
Subject Heading: BIBLE–STUDY \ DISCIPLESHIP \ PRAYER

Printed in the United States of America

Student Ministry Publishing
LifeWay Church Resources
One LifeWay Plaza
Nashville, TN 37234-0174

Unless otherwise noted, all Scripture quotations are taken from the
Holman Christian Standard Bible® copyright © 1999, 2000, 2002, 2003
by Holman Bible Publishers.
Used by permission.

Scripture quotations marked NIV are from the *Holy Bible, New International
Version,* copyright © 1973, 1978, 1984 by International Bible Society.

How to Use DiscipleHelps

THIS JOURNAL IS A TOOL TO HELP YOU GROW toward Christian maturity. Use the pages of this journal to explore your relationship with Jesus Christ and to reflect on the things He is teaching you as you travel through life with Him.

This journal is designed to last for three months. Each week, you will: (1) record your prayer concerns, (2) develop other areas of your prayer life: thanksgiving, adoration, and confession, (3) note a memory verse you are working on for the week, (4) dig into personal daily Bible study, and (5) reflect on your study of God's Word with other believers. Each page is designed to be flexible and easy to use. You might not use your journal exactly as your best friend does; all of us will approach our walk with Christ a little differently.

Your Daily Quiet Time

When you committed your life to Jesus Christ, you became one of His children. This relationship with God enables you to have fellowship with Him. Although your relationship with God is constant, your fellowship with Him will vary with your obedience to His leadership. A quiet time can help you maintain fellowship with God. A quiet time is daily time with God that includes studying and memorizing His Word and prayer. Daily time with God will help you build spiritual strength, become sensitive to God's leadership, and apply His Word to your life.

Getting Started

Step 1: Make a Commitment to a Daily Quiet Time
Decide that your quiet time will be your first priority each day. Some people say they will not eat until they have first had the spiritual nourishment from their quiet time. Make up your mind that you won't make excuses.

Step 2: Develop a Plan for Your Daily Quiet Time
Decide when and where you will have your quiet time. It is best to schedule it first thing in the morning. Beginning the day with God will make a difference in your whole day. The best place for your quiet time will be some place free of distractions. You might choose a place in your room or even outdoors when the weather permits. Make sure you can read the Bible, pray, and make notes easily.

God will use your quiet time to make a huge difference in your life if you don't give up. If you miss your quiet time one day, start again the next. Your quiet time will be more meaningful on some days. Don't expect every quiet time to put you on a spiritual high. Stay consistent and you will be amazed at what God does in your life.

Prayer List

GOD IS CONCERNED ABOUT EVERYTHING that concerns you. When you have a test coming up at school, when a friend hurts your feelings, when you are concerned about a problem someone you know is facing . . . at all of those times, God shares your concern. He wants you to talk to Him about your concerns for your own life and for your friends and family.

Even beyond your personal concerns, the more you get to know God, the more you will develop a heart for the world. When there is a crisis in another part of the world, the Holy Spirit will tug at your heart and prompt you to ask God to be at work in the situation. When you meet someone who is clearly lost, the Holy Spirit will prompt you to pray for her, too.

On the next page you will see an example of a weekly prayer list. Notice that it begins with a space to write a weekly Scripture memory verse. During your quiet time each day, turn to this page. Review your Scripture memory verse each day and then dive into your prayer list.

Add prayer concerns all week long. When you get to the end of the week, you will want to copy some of the requests onto the next week's prayer list. Some prayer requests may be on your prayer list for months.

Don't try to write out everything you want to say; just use a few words to remind yourself to keep praying for a specific need in your life, in a friend's life, or in the world. Be careful not to write anything that would embarrass a friend if someone else found your journal. If someone shares a prayer request in confidence, write the request so that it would not mean anything to anyone else. For example, the teen in the example on the next page was praying for someone she calls "S." We don't know anymore than that.

Writing a request is only a reminder to pray. It doesn't mean anything unless you take time to talk to God about your requests on a consistent basis. Don't tell someone you will pray for them unless you really will. Prayer may seem like an easy thing to do, but real prayer can be work—concentration, emotional energy, and even spiritual warfare. Don't take your prayer time lightly. Someone once said, "Prayer is not preparation for the work; prayer is the work."

SELECT A VERSE TO MEMORIZE EACH WEEK AND WRITE IT IN THE PROVIDED SPACE.

CREATE A LIST OF PEOPLE AND SITUATIONS YOU ARE PRAYING FOR DURING THE WEEK.

THERE IS NO NEED TO WRITE COMPLETE SENTENCES. WRITE WORDS OR PHRASES THAT REMIND YOU OF THE REQUEST.

DON'T WRITE ANYTHING THAT WOULD EMBARRASS A FRIEND IF SOMEONE FOUND YOUR JOURNAL.

YOU CAN PLACE AN X IN THE BOX WHEN GOD HAS ANSWERED YOUR PRAYER REQUEST.

WEEK 1

FOR THE WEEK OF _____NOVEMBER 3_____ TO _NOVEMBER 10, 2004_

MEMORY VERSE_Therefore, no condemnation now exists for_
those in Christ Jesus (Rom. 8:1).

MY PRAYER LIST

- ☐ Improved relationship with Dad
- ☒ Algebra test on Friday
- ☐ Sally – money for summer camp
- ☐ Joe – to become a Christian
- ☐ The Ingrams, missionaries in Africa
- ☒ Mom – help her feel better
- ☐ My witness on the team
- ☐ S. – the problem she shared with me
- ☐ _____

"GOD HAS GUARANTEED YOUR INHERITANCE WITH THE DOWN PAYMENT OF HIS HOLY SPIRIT. YOU ARE A CITIZEN OF HEAVEN AND A SERVANT OF GOD."

–C. Gene Wilkes

C. Gene Wilkes, *My Identity in Christ, Student Edition* (Nashville: LifeWay Press, 2000), 119.

Personal Prayer Time

GOD DOES WANT US TO BRING OUR REQUESTS to Him. However, prayer is a lot more than asking God for help. As you talk with God each day, your conversation should involve prayers for yourself and prayers for others. They should also include each of these three kinds of prayer.

READ THE PRAISE VERSE AS A PRAYER TO GOD.

A. Praise

Praise is closely related to thanksgiving, but there is a difference. Praise is adoring God for who He is. Thanksgiving is thanking God for what He has done. Praise is showing love to God. Thanksgiving is expressing gratitude. God is to be praised for His character. He is to be thanked for His actions.

Each week, there will be a verse of Scripture that should prompt you to express your love to God. Often you can read the verse as a prayer to God. There is a space provided each week for you to write words or phrases that are important to you as you express your praise.

WRITE WORDS OR PHRASES THAT ARE IMPORTANT TO YOU AS YOU EXPRESS PRAISE.

B. Thanksgiving

Each week there also will be a verse of Scripture to lead you to reflect on the things God has done in your life. Express your thankfulness for specific things. Cultivate a general attitude of thankfulness whatever the circumstance. (See 1 Thess. 5:18.) There is a space provided to write things you are thankful for.

WRITE THINGS YOU ARE THANKFUL FOR.

C. Confession

Each week you will see a verse of Scripture regarding the need for confession of sin. Read this verse each day and use it to begin your time of confession. Then do the following.

USE THE CONFESSION VERSE TO PROMPT A TIME OF PERSONAL CONFESSION OF SINS.

- Ask the Lord to make you aware of any sins that are hurting your fellowship with Him.
- Confess each sin individually to the Lord. Agree with God that the sin is wrong.
- Express your desire to avoid these sins in the future.
- Claim by faith His forgiveness.
- Right the wrong to whatever extent you can.
- Accept by faith the fact that you are totally cleansed. (See 1 John 1:9.)

Use the space after the confession verse to write thoughts or brief prayers as you confess your sins to God.

WRITE THOUGHTS OR BRIEF PRAYERS AS YOU CONFESS YOUR SINS TO GOD.

WEEK 1

Personal Prayer

PRAISE

Wake up, harp and lyre! I will wake up the dawn. I will praise You, Lord, among the peoples; I will sing praises to You among the nations (Ps. 108:2-3).

God is my Mighty Defender. You are my hope, Lord Jesus.

THANKSGIVING

Give thanks in everything, for this is God's will for you in Christ Jesus (1 Thess. 5:18).

Friends, my family, an A in English, speaking to me at church on Sunday, my best friend. food to eat, the special time with my dad.

CONFESSION

Therefore do not let sin reign in your mortal body, so that you obey its desires. And do not offer any parts of it to sin as weapons for unrighteousness. But as those who are alive from the dead, offer yourselves to God, and all the parts of yourselves to God as weapons for righteousness (Rom. 6:12-13).

God, I blew it again last night; help me to get my temper under control. Forgive me for looking at things I shouldn't have. Lord, I'm having the same problem with taking my parents for granted. I gave into that old temptation again; I'm sorry, Lord.

Personal Bible Study

TO GROW AS A CHRISTIAN, YOU NEED TO STUDY God's Word for yourself. Use one of the Personal Bible Study sheets each day as a guide to get into God's Word.

Begin by reading a selected passage. If you aren't sure what to read, choose a book of the Bible and work your way through it reading a short passage each day. You might start with John or Proverbs.

As you read, notice the key ideas in the passage. Write them in your journal. Ask yourself, *What is this passage really trying to say?* You may find one key idea or many.

Look for ways to apply the passage to your life. Is there something you need to do, think about, or strive to be? Is there an example to follow or an example to avoid? Write your thoughts under "Application." You might include a sentence of prayer as a response to God.

Before you leave a passage, summarize it in one sentence. This will help you get a grasp on what you have been reading. Avoid just giving a one-word summary. *Love* might be what the passage is about, but that word only gives you the subject, not the truth of the passage. This activity will take some thought, but it will help you to understand the passage.

Finally, write specific questions or thoughts you want to study further. You may ask your youth leader about your questions. You might do further research in the library or on the Internet.

Group Bible Study

HEARING GOD'S WORD in sermons or Bible study classes is also essential if you want to grasp God's Word. Real listening requires concentration and effort on your part. You will forget most of what you hear—unless you write it down.

Your journal includes a Group Bible Study page each week. The page will give you a place to record the same kind of information you do in Personal Bible Study for those times you are studying the Bible with others.

WRITE THE DATE OF YOUR BIBLE STUDY AND THE PASSAGE YOU ARE STUDYING.

KEY IDEAS: NOTE THE KEY IDEAS OF THE PASSAGE IN THIS SECTION.

APPLICATION: WRITE SPECIFIC WAYS THAT THESE CONCEPTS APPLY TO YOUR LIFE.

SUMMARY: WRITE THE TRUTH OF THE PASSAGE YOU READ IN ONE SENTENCE.

QUESTIONS: WRITE QUESTIONS YOU HAVE OR THOUGHTS YOU WANT TO STUDY FURTHER.

Personal Bible Study 1

DATE _November 6, 2004_

SCRIPTURE PASSAGE _Matthew 13:31-33_

KEY IDEAS

God's kingdom often starts small and grows. It is also like yeast that sort of works its way through everything it touches.

APPLICATION

I need to realize that little things matter. God's kingdom is less about big events and more about the way I live day by day. Father, help me to live today with the little things in mind.

SUMMARY

The kingdom of God may start little, but it will grow.

QUESTIONS

I should learn more about the kingdom of God. Also, I wonder how yeast really works.

WEEK 1

FOR THE WEEK OF _____ TO _____

MEMORY VERSE _____

_____

_____

MY PRAYER LIST

☐ _____

☐ _____

☐ _____

☐ _____

☐ _____

☐ _____

☐ _____

☐ _____

☐ _____

"GOD HAS GUARANTEED YOUR INHERITANCE WITH THE DOWN PAYMENT OF HIS HOLY SPIRIT. YOU ARE A CITIZEN OF HEAVEN AND A SERVANT OF GOD."

–C. Gene Wilkes

C. Gene Wilkes, *My Identity in Christ, Student Edition* (Nashville: LifeWay Press, 2000), 119.

Personal Prayer

PRAISE

Wake up, harp and lyre! I will wake up the dawn. I will praise You, Lord, among the peoples; I will sing praises to You among the nations (Ps. 108:2-3).

_____

_____

_____

THANKSGIVING

Give thanks in everything, for this is God's will for you in Christ Jesus (1 Thess. 5:18).

_____

_____

_____

_____

_____

CONFESSION

Therefore do not let sin reign in your mortal body, so that you obey its desires. And do not offer any parts of it to sin as weapons for unrighteousness. But as those who are alive from the dead, offer yourselves to God, and all the parts of yourselves to God as weapons for righteousness (Rom. 6:12-13).

_____

_____

_____

Personal Bible Study 1

DATE ————————

SCRIPTURE PASSAGE ————————

KEY IDEAS

————————

————————

————————

APPLICATION

————————

————————

————————

SUMMARY

————————

————————

————————

QUESTIONS

————————

————————

————————

Personal Bible Study 2

DATE _____

SCRIPTURE PASSAGE _____

KEY IDEAS

_____

_____

_____

APPLICATION

_____

_____

_____

_____

SUMMARY

_____

_____

_____

_____

QUESTIONS

_____

_____

_____

_____

Personal Bible Study 3

DATE ——————————————

SCRIPTURE PASSAGE ——————————————

KEY IDEAS

——————————————————————

——————————————————————

——————————————————————

APPLICATION

——————————————————————

——————————————————————

——————————————————————

——————————————————————

SUMMARY

——————————————————————

——————————————————————

——————————————————————

——————————————————————

QUESTIONS

——————————————————————

——————————————————————

——————————————————————

——————————————————————

Personal Bible Study 4

DATE _____

SCRIPTURE PASSAGE _____

KEY IDEAS

_____

_____

_____

APPLICATION

_____

_____

_____

_____

SUMMARY

_____

_____

_____

_____

QUESTIONS

_____

_____

_____

_____

Personal Bible Study 5

DATE _____

SCRIPTURE PASSAGE _____

KEY IDEAS

_____

_____

_____

APPLICATION

_____

_____

_____

_____

SUMMARY

_____

_____

_____

_____

QUESTIONS

_____

_____

_____

_____

Personal Bible Study 6

DATE _____

SCRIPTURE PASSAGE_____

KEY IDEAS

_____

APPLICATION

_____

SUMMARY

_____

QUESTIONS

_____

Personal Bible Study 7

DATE _____

SCRIPTURE PASSAGE_____

KEY IDEAS

_____

APPLICATION

_____

SUMMARY

_____

QUESTIONS

_____

Group Bible Study

DATE ————————————

SCRIPTURE PASSAGE————————————

KEY IDEAS

————————————————

————————————————

————————————————

APPLICATION

————————————————

————————————————

————————————————

————————————————

SUMMARY

————————————————

————————————————

————————————————

————————————————

QUESTIONS

————————————————

————————————————

————————————————

————————————————

WEEK 2

FOR THE WEEK OF _____ TO _____

MEMORY VERSE _____

_____

_____

MY PRAYER LIST

☐ _____

☐ _____

☐ _____

☐ _____

☐ _____

☐ _____

☐ _____

☐ _____

☐ _____

"MOST CHRISTIANS FOR MOST OF THE CHRISTIAN CENTURIES HAVE LEARNED TO PRAY BY PRAYING THE PSALMS."

–Eugene H. Peterson

Eugene H. Peterson, *The Message: Psalms* (Colorado Springs: NavPress, 1994), 5.

Personal Prayer

Praise

Lift up your heads, O gates! Rise up, O ancient doors! Then the King of glory will come in. Who is He, this King of glory? The Lord of Hosts, He is the King of glory (Ps. 24:9-10).

Thanksgiving

Acknowledge that the Lord is God. He made us, and we are His—His people, the sheep of His pasture. Enter His gates with thanksgiving and His courts with praise. Give thanks to Him and praise His name (Ps. 100:3-4).

Confession

Test me, Lord, and try me; examine my heart and mind (Ps. 26:2).

Personal Bible Study 1

DATE ⸻⸻

SCRIPTURE PASSAGE ⸻⸻

KEY IDEAS

⸻⸻⸻⸻
⸻⸻⸻⸻
⸻⸻⸻⸻

APPLICATION

⸻⸻⸻⸻
⸻⸻⸻⸻
⸻⸻⸻⸻
⸻⸻⸻⸻

SUMMARY

⸻⸻⸻⸻
⸻⸻⸻⸻
⸻⸻⸻⸻
⸻⸻⸻⸻

QUESTIONS

⸻⸻⸻⸻
⸻⸻⸻⸻
⸻⸻⸻⸻
⸻⸻⸻⸻

Personal Bible Study 2

DATE ————————————

SCRIPTURE PASSAGE————————————

KEY IDEAS

————————————————

————————————————

————————————————

APPLICATION

————————————————

————————————————

————————————————

SUMMARY

————————————————

————————————————

————————————————

————————————————

QUESTIONS

————————————————

————————————————

————————————————

————————————————

Personal Bible Study 3

DATE _____

SCRIPTURE PASSAGE_____

KEY IDEAS

_____

_____

_____

APPLICATION

_____

_____

_____

SUMMARY

_____

_____

_____

QUESTIONS

_____

_____

_____

Personal Bible Study 4

DATE _____

SCRIPTURE PASSAGE_____

KEY IDEAS

_____

_____

_____

APPLICATION

_____

_____

_____

SUMMARY

_____

_____

_____

QUESTIONS

_____

_____

_____

_____

Personal Bible Study 5

DATE _____

SCRIPTURE PASSAGE_____

KEY IDEAS

_____

_____

_____

APPLICATION

_____

_____

_____

_____

SUMMARY

_____

_____

_____

_____

QUESTIONS

_____

_____

_____

_____

Personal Bible Study 6

DATE _____

SCRIPTURE PASSAGE_____

KEY IDEAS

APPLICATION

SUMMARY

QUESTIONS

Personal Bible Study 7

DATE _____

SCRIPTURE PASSAGE_____

KEY IDEAS

APPLICATION

SUMMARY

QUESTIONS

Group Bible Study

DATE _____

SCRIPTURE PASSAGE _____

KEY IDEAS

_____

_____

_____

APPLICATION

_____

_____

_____

_____

SUMMARY

_____

_____

_____

_____

QUESTIONS

_____

_____

_____

_____

WEEK 3

FOR THE WEEK OF _____ TO_____

MEMORY VERSE _____

_____

_____

MY PRAYER LIST

☐ _____

☐ _____

☐ _____

☐ _____

☐ _____

☐ _____

☐ _____

☐ _____

☐ _____

"EVERYTHING THAT SCRIPTURE TEACHES US TO BELIEVE AND TO BE AND TO DO CONTAINS ONE COMMON THREAD: AN INTIMATE, REAL RELATIONSHIP WITH THE ONE TRUE GOD OF THE UNIVERSE."

–Josh McDowell

Josh McDowell with Bob Hostetler, *Beyond Belief to Convictions* (Wheaton, Ill.: Tyndale House Publishers, 2002), 32.

Personal Prayer

PRAISE

Lord, the heavens praise Your wonders—Your faithfulness also—in the assembly of the holy ones. For who in the skies can compare with the Lord? Who among the heavenly beings is like the Lord? God is greatly feared in the council of the holy ones, more awe-inspiring than all who surround Him. O Lord God of Hosts, who is strong like You, Lord? Your faithfulness surrounds You (Ps. 89:5-8).

THANKSGIVING

But thanks be to God, who always puts us on display in Christ, and spreads through us in every place the scent of knowing Him (2 Cor. 2:14).

CONFESSION

My little children, I am writing you these things so that you may not sin. But if anyone does sin, we have an advocate with the Father—Jesus Christ the righteous One. He Himself is the propitiation for our sins, and not only for ours, but also for those of the whole world (1 John 2:1-2).

Personal Bible Study 1

DATE _____

SCRIPTURE PASSAGE_____

KEY IDEAS

_____

_____

_____

APPLICATION

_____

_____

_____

_____

SUMMARY

_____

_____

_____

_____

QUESTIONS

_____

_____

_____

_____

Personal Bible Study 2

DATE _____

SCRIPTURE PASSAGE _____

KEY IDEAS

_____

_____

_____

APPLICATION

_____

_____

_____

_____

SUMMARY

_____

_____

_____

_____

QUESTIONS

_____

_____

_____

_____

Personal Bible Study 3

DATE _____

SCRIPTURE PASSAGE_____

KEY IDEAS

_____

_____

_____

APPLICATION

_____

_____

_____

_____

SUMMARY

_____

_____

_____

_____

QUESTIONS

_____

_____

_____

_____

Personal Bible Study 4

Date _____

Scripture Passage _____

KEY IDEAS

_____

_____

_____

APPLICATION

_____

_____

_____

_____

SUMMARY

_____

_____

_____

_____

QUESTIONS

_____

_____

_____

_____

Personal Bible Study 5

DATE _____

SCRIPTURE PASSAGE _____

KEY IDEAS

_____

_____

_____

APPLICATION

_____

_____

_____

_____

SUMMARY

_____

_____

_____

_____

QUESTIONS

_____

_____

_____

_____

Personal Bible Study 6

DATE _____

SCRIPTURE PASSAGE_____

KEY IDEAS

_____

APPLICATION

_____

SUMMARY

_____

QUESTIONS

_____

Personal Bible Study 7

DATE _____

SCRIPTURE PASSAGE_____

KEY IDEAS

_____

APPLICATION

_____

SUMMARY

_____

QUESTIONS

_____

Group Bible Study

DATE _____

SCRIPTURE PASSAGE _____

KEY IDEAS

_____

_____

_____

APPLICATION

_____

_____

_____

SUMMARY

_____

_____

_____

QUESTIONS

_____

_____

_____

_____

WEEK 4

FOR THE WEEK OF _____ TO_____

MEMORY VERSE _____

_____

_____

MY PRAYER LIST

☐ _____

☐ _____

☐ _____

☐ _____

☐ _____

☐ _____

☐ _____

☐ _____

☐ _____

"PRAYER IS COMMUNICATING WITH GOD IN A WAY THAT MAKES YOU AWARE OF HIS PRESENCE."

–Gene Mims

Gene Mims, *The Kingdom-Focused Church* (Nashville: Broadman and Holman Publishers, 2003), 121.

Personal Prayer

PRAISE

My soul, praise the Lord, and all that is within me, praise His holy name. My soul, praise the Lord, and do not forget all His benefits. He forgives all your sin; He heals all your diseases. He redeems your life from the Pit; He crowns you with faithful love and compassion. He satisfies you with goodness; your youth is renewed like the eagle (Ps. 103:1-5).

THANKSGIVING

We give thanks to You, God; we give thanks to You, for Your name is near. People tell about Your wonderful works (Ps. 75:1).

CONFESSION

Don't be deceived: God is not mocked. For whatever a man sows he will also reap, because the one who sows to his flesh will reap corruption from the flesh, but the one who sows to the Spirit will reap eternal life from the Spirit. So we must not get tired of doing good, for we will reap at the proper time if we don't give up (Gal. 6:7-8).

Personal Bible Study 1

DATE _____

SCRIPTURE PASSAGE _____

KEY IDEAS

_____

_____

_____

APPLICATION

_____

_____

_____

_____

SUMMARY

_____

_____

_____

_____

QUESTIONS

_____

_____

_____

_____

Personal Bible Study 2

DATE _____

SCRIPTURE PASSAGE_____

KEY IDEAS

_____

_____

_____

APPLICATION

_____

_____

_____

_____

SUMMARY

_____

_____

_____

_____

QUESTIONS

_____

_____

_____

_____

Personal Bible Study 3

DATE _____

SCRIPTURE PASSAGE_____

KEY IDEAS

_____

_____

_____

APPLICATION

_____

_____

_____

_____

SUMMARY

_____

_____

_____

_____

QUESTIONS

_____

_____

_____

_____

Personal Bible Study 4

DATE _____

SCRIPTURE PASSAGE_____

KEY IDEAS

_____

_____

_____

APPLICATION

_____

_____

_____

_____

SUMMARY

_____

_____

_____

_____

QUESTIONS

_____

_____

_____

_____

Personal Bible Study 5

DATE _____

SCRIPTURE PASSAGE _____

KEY IDEAS

_____

_____

_____

APPLICATION

_____

_____

_____

_____

SUMMARY

_____

_____

_____

_____

QUESTIONS

_____

_____

_____

_____

Personal Bible Study 6

DATE _____

SCRIPTURE PASSAGE _____

KEY IDEAS

_____

APPLICATION

_____

SUMMARY

_____

QUESTIONS

_____

Personal Bible Study 7

DATE _____

SCRIPTURE PASSAGE _____

KEY IDEAS

_____

APPLICATION

_____

SUMMARY

_____

QUESTIONS

_____

Group Bible Study

DATE _____

SCRIPTURE PASSAGE _____

KEY IDEAS

_____

_____

_____

APPLICATION

_____

_____

_____

_____

SUMMARY

_____

_____

_____

_____

QUESTIONS

_____

_____

_____

_____

WEEK 5

FOR THE WEEK OF _____ TO_____

MEMORY VERSE _____

_____

_____

MY PRAYER LIST

- ☐ _____
- ☐ _____
- ☐ _____
- ☐ _____
- ☐ _____
- ☐ _____
- ☐ _____
- ☐ _____

"OF ALL THE GIFTS GOD GIVES US, SURELY THE MOST

PRECIOUS IS THE GIFT OF TIME. . . . IT IS SO

PRECIOUS THAT WHEN WE GIVE IT BACK TO GOD IT SETS

THE ANGELS AT THEIR ALLELUIAS."

–Calvin Miller

Calvin Miller, *Into the Depths of God* (Bloomington, Minn.: Bethany Press International, 2000), 47.

Personal Prayer

PRAISE

My soul, praise the Lord! Lord my God, You are very great; You are clothed with majesty and splendor. He wraps Himself in light as if it were a robe, spreading out the sky like a canopy, laying the beams of His palace on the waters above, making the clouds His chariot, walking on the wings of the wind, and making the winds His messengers, flames of fire His servants (Ps. 104:1-4).

———————————————————————————————

———————————————————————————————

———————————————————————————————

THANKSGIVING

But we must always thank God for you, brothers loved by the Lord, because from the beginning God has chosen you for salvation through sanctification by the Spirit and through belief in the truth (2 Thess. 2:13).

———————————————————————————————

———————————————————————————————

———————————————————————————————

———————————————————————————————

CONFESSION

So if you are offering your gift on the altar, and there you remember that your brother has something against you, leave your gift there in front of the altar. First go and be reconciled with your brother, and then come and offer your gift (Matt. 5:23-24).

———————————————————————————————

———————————————————————————————

———————————————————————————————

Personal Bible Study 1

DATE _____

SCRIPTURE PASSAGE_____

KEY IDEAS

_____

_____

_____

APPLICATION

_____

_____

_____

_____

SUMMARY

_____

_____

_____

_____

QUESTIONS

_____

_____

_____

_____

Personal Bible Study 2

DATE _____

SCRIPTURE PASSAGE_____

KEY IDEAS

_____

_____

_____

APPLICATION

_____

_____

_____

_____

SUMMARY

_____

_____

_____

_____

QUESTIONS

_____

_____

_____

_____

Personal Bible Study 3

DATE _____

SCRIPTURE PASSAGE_____

KEY IDEAS

_____

_____

_____

APPLICATION

_____

_____

_____

_____

SUMMARY

_____

_____

_____

_____

QUESTIONS

_____

_____

_____

_____

Personal Bible Study 4

DATE _____

SCRIPTURE PASSAGE_____

KEY IDEAS

_____

_____

_____

APPLICATION

_____

_____

_____

_____

SUMMARY

_____

_____

_____

_____

QUESTIONS

_____

_____

_____

_____

Personal Bible Study 5

DATE _____

SCRIPTURE PASSAGE_____

KEY IDEAS

_____

_____

_____

APPLICATION

_____

_____

_____

SUMMARY

_____

_____

_____

QUESTIONS

_____

_____

_____

Personal Bible Study 6

DATE _____

SCRIPTURE PASSAGE_____

KEY IDEAS

_____

APPLICATION

_____

SUMMARY

_____

QUESTIONS

_____

Personal Bible Study 7

DATE _____

SCRIPTURE PASSAGE_____

KEY IDEAS

_____

APPLICATION

_____

SUMMARY

_____

QUESTIONS

_____

Group Bible Study

DATE _____

SCRIPTURE PASSAGE_____

KEY IDEAS

_____

_____

_____

APPLICATION

_____

_____

_____

_____

SUMMARY

_____

_____

_____

_____

QUESTIONS

_____

_____

_____

_____

WEEK 6

For the Week of _____ to_____

Memory Verse _____

_____

_____

MY PRAYER LIST

☐ _____

☐ _____

☐ _____

☐ _____

☐ _____

☐ _____

☐ _____

☐ _____

☐ _____

"HE THAT FORGETS HIS FRIEND, IS UNGRATEFUL

UNTO HIM; BUT HE THAT FORGETS HIS SAVIOR,

IS UNMERCIFUL TO HIMSELF."

–John Bunyon

John Bunyon, *The Pilgrim's Progress* (Grand Rapids, Mich.: Baker Book House, 1967), 251.

Personal Prayer

PRAISE

Hallelujah! Give thanks to the Lord, for He is good; His faithful love endures forever. Who can declare the Lord's mighty acts or proclaim all the praise due Him? How happy are those who uphold justice, who practice righteousness at all times (Ps. 106:1-3).

_____

_____

_____

THANKSGIVING

When Daniel learned that the document had been signed, he went into his house. The windows in its upper room opened toward Jerusalem, and three times a day he got down on his knees, prayed, and gave thanks to his God, just as he had done before (Dan. 6:10).

_____

_____

_____

_____

CONFESSION

Be gracious to me, God, according to Your faithful love; according to Your abundant compassion, blot out my rebellion. Wash away my guilt, and cleanse me from my sin (Ps. 51:1-2).

_____

_____

_____

Personal Bible Study 1

DATE _____

SCRIPTURE PASSAGE_____

KEY IDEAS

_____

_____

_____

APPLICATION

_____

_____

_____

_____

SUMMARY

_____

_____

_____

_____

QUESTIONS

_____

_____

_____

_____

Personal Bible Study 2

DATE _____

SCRIPTURE PASSAGE_____

KEY IDEAS

_____

_____

_____

APPLICATION

_____

_____

_____

_____

SUMMARY

_____

_____

_____

QUESTIONS

_____

_____

_____

_____

Personal Bible Study 3

DATE _____

SCRIPTURE PASSAGE_____

KEY IDEAS

_____

_____

_____

APPLICATION

_____

_____

_____

_____

SUMMARY

_____

_____

_____

_____

QUESTIONS

_____

_____

_____

_____

Personal Bible Study 4

DATE _____

SCRIPTURE PASSAGE_____

KEY IDEAS

_____

_____

_____

APPLICATION

_____

_____

_____

_____

SUMMARY

_____

_____

_____

_____

QUESTIONS

_____

_____

_____

_____

Personal Bible Study 5

DATE _____

SCRIPTURE PASSAGE_____

KEY IDEAS

_____

_____

_____

APPLICATION

_____

_____

_____

_____

SUMMARY

_____

_____

_____

_____

QUESTIONS

_____

_____

_____

_____

Personal Bible Study 6

DATE _____

SCRIPTURE PASSAGE _____

KEY IDEAS

_____

APPLICATION

_____

SUMMARY

_____

QUESTIONS

_____

Personal Bible Study 7

DATE _____

SCRIPTURE PASSAGE _____

KEY IDEAS

_____

APPLICATION

_____

SUMMARY

_____

QUESTIONS

_____

Group Bible Study

DATE _____

SCRIPTURE PASSAGE_____

KEY IDEAS

_____

_____

_____

APPLICATION

_____

_____

_____

_____

SUMMARY

_____

_____

_____

_____

QUESTIONS

_____

_____

_____

_____

WEEK 7

FOR THE WEEK OF _____ TO_____

MEMORY VERSE _____

_____

_____

MY PRAYER LIST

☐ _____

☐ _____

☐ _____

☐ _____

☐ _____

☐ _____

☐ _____

☐ _____

☐ _____

"WE WANT GOD-ESTEEM, NOT SELF-ESTEEM. AND WHO DOES GOD ESTEEM? 'HE WHO IS HUMBLE AND CONTRITE IN SPIRIT, AND TREMBLES AT MY WORD.' (ISAIAH 66:2B NIV)"

–James R. Lucas

James R. Lucas, *Am I the One?* (Nashville: Broadman and Holman Publishers, 2002), 25.

Personal Prayer

PRAISE

Hallelujah! I will praise the Lord with all my heart in the assembly of the upright and in the congregation. The Lord's works are great, studied by all who delight in them. All that He does is splendid and majestic; His righteousness endures forever (Ps. 111:1-3).

THANKSGIVING

Don't worry about anything, but in everything, through prayer and petition with thanksgiving, let your requests be made known to God (Phil. 4:6).

CONFESSION

For we do not have a high priest who is unable to sympathize with our weaknesses, but One who has been tested in every way as we are, yet without sin. Therefore let us approach the throne of grace with boldness, so that we may receive mercy and find grace to help us at the proper time (Heb. 4:15-16).

Personal Bible Study 1

DATE _____

SCRIPTURE PASSAGE_____

KEY IDEAS

_____

_____

_____

APPLICATION

_____

_____

_____

_____

SUMMARY

_____

_____

_____

_____

QUESTIONS

_____

_____

_____

_____

Personal Bible Study 2

DATE _____

SCRIPTURE PASSAGE _____

KEY IDEAS

_____

_____

_____

APPLICATION

_____

_____

_____

_____

SUMMARY

_____

_____

_____

_____

QUESTIONS

_____

_____

_____

_____

Personal Bible Study 3

DATE _____

SCRIPTURE PASSAGE_____

KEY IDEAS

_____

_____

_____

APPLICATION

_____

_____

_____

_____

SUMMARY

_____

_____

_____

_____

QUESTIONS

_____

_____

_____

_____

Personal Bible Study 4

DATE _____

SCRIPTURE PASSAGE_____

KEY IDEAS

_____

_____

_____

APPLICATION

_____

_____

_____

_____

SUMMARY

_____

_____

_____

_____

QUESTIONS

_____

_____

_____

_____

Personal Bible Study 5

DATE _____

SCRIPTURE PASSAGE_____

KEY IDEAS

_____

_____

_____

APPLICATION

_____

_____

_____

_____

SUMMARY

_____

_____

_____

QUESTIONS

_____

_____

_____

_____

Personal Bible Study 6

DATE _____

SCRIPTURE PASSAGE_____

KEY IDEAS

_____

APPLICATION

_____

SUMMARY

_____

QUESTIONS

_____

Personal Bible Study 7

DATE _____

SCRIPTURE PASSAGE_____

KEY IDEAS

_____

APPLICATION

_____

SUMMARY

_____

QUESTIONS

_____

Group Bible Study

DATE _____

SCRIPTURE PASSAGE_____

KEY IDEAS

_____

_____

_____

APPLICATION

_____

_____

_____

_____

SUMMARY

_____

_____

_____

_____

QUESTIONS

_____

_____

_____

_____

WEEK 8

FOR THE WEEK OF _____ TO_____

MEMORY VERSE _____

_____

_____

MY PRAYER LIST

☐ _____

☐ _____

☐ _____

☐ _____

☐ _____

☐ _____

☐ _____

☐ _____

"THE CHRISTIAN IS LIKE THE ATHLETE.
THE HEAVIER THE COURSE OF TRAINING HE
UNDERGOES, THE MORE HE IS GLAD, BECAUSE HE
KNOWS THAT IT IS FITTING HIM ALL THE BETTER
FOR VICTORIOUS EFFORT."

–William Barclay

William Barclay, *The Daily Study Bible Series: The Letters of James and Peter*, rev. ed. (Philadelphia: The Westminster Press, 1976), 43.

Personal Prayer

PRAISE

Praise the LORD, all nations! Glorify Him, all peoples! For great is His faithful love to us; the Lord's faithfulness endures forever. Hallelujah! (Ps. 117).

_____

_____

_____

THANKSGIVING

I rise at midnight to thank You for Your righteous judgments (Ps. 119:62)

_____

_____

_____

_____

_____

CONFESSION

No temptation has overtaken you except what is common to humanity. God is faithful and He will not allow you to be tempted beyond what you are able, but with the temptation He will also provide a way of escape, so that you are able to bear it (1 Cor. 10:13).

_____

_____

_____

_____

_____

Personal Bible Study 1

DATE _____

SCRIPTURE PASSAGE_____

KEY IDEAS

_____

_____

_____

APPLICATION

_____

_____

_____

_____

SUMMARY

_____

_____

_____

_____

QUESTIONS

_____

_____

_____

_____

Personal Bible Study 2

DATE _____

SCRIPTURE PASSAGE_____

KEY IDEAS

_____

_____

_____

APPLICATION

_____

_____

_____

SUMMARY

_____

_____

_____

QUESTIONS

_____

_____

_____

Personal Bible Study 3

Date _____

Scripture Passage_____

KEY IDEAS

_____
_____
_____

APPLICATION

_____
_____
_____
_____

SUMMARY

_____
_____
_____
_____

QUESTIONS

_____
_____
_____
_____

Personal Bible Study 4

DATE _____

SCRIPTURE PASSAGE_____

KEY IDEAS

_____

_____

_____

APPLICATION

_____

_____

_____

_____

SUMMARY

_____

_____

_____

_____

QUESTIONS

_____

_____

_____

_____

Personal Bible Study 5

DATE _____

SCRIPTURE PASSAGE_____

KEY IDEAS

_____

_____

_____

APPLICATION

_____

_____

_____

_____

SUMMARY

_____

_____

_____

_____

QUESTIONS

_____

_____

_____

_____

Personal Bible Study 6

DATE _____

SCRIPTURE PASSAGE_____

KEY IDEAS

_____

APPLICATION

_____

SUMMARY

_____

QUESTIONS

_____

Personal Bible Study 7

DATE _____

SCRIPTURE PASSAGE_____

KEY IDEAS

_____

APPLICATION

_____

SUMMARY

_____

QUESTIONS

_____

Group Bible Study

DATE _____

SCRIPTURE PASSAGE_____

KEY IDEAS

_____

_____

_____

APPLICATION

_____

_____

_____

_____

SUMMARY

_____

_____

_____

_____

QUESTIONS

_____

_____

_____

_____

WEEK 9

For the Week of _____ to _____

Memory Verse _____

_____

_____

My Prayer List

☐ _____

☐ _____

☐ _____

☐ _____

☐ _____

☐ _____

☐ _____

☐ _____

"At the end of myself, I came to the beginning of an intensity of relationship with an invisible Savior that no one had ever told me existed. In crude terms, I think He's a blast."

–Beth Moore

Beth Moore, *John: The Beloved Disciple, Student Edition* (Nashville: LifeWay Press, 2003), 44.

Personal Prayer

PRAISE

Hallelujah! Praise the name of the Lord. Give praise, you servants of the Lord who stand in the house of the Lord, in the courts of the house of our God. Praise the Lord, for the Lord is good; sing praise to His name, for it is delightful (Ps. 135:1-3).

_____

_____

_____

THANKSGIVING

Then He commanded the crowd to sit down on the ground. Taking the seven loaves, He gave thanks, broke the loaves, and kept on giving them to His disciples to set before them. So they served the loaves to the crowd (Mark 8:6).

_____

_____

_____

_____

_____

CONFESSION

If you love Me, you will keep My commandments. And I will ask the Father, and He will give you another Counselor to be with you forever. He is the Spirit of truth, whom the world is unable to receive because it doesn't see Him or know Him. But you do know Him, because He remains with you and will be in you (John 14:15-17).

_____

_____

_____

Personal Bible Study 1

DATE _____

SCRIPTURE PASSAGE_____

KEY IDEAS

_____

_____

_____

APPLICATION

_____

_____

_____

SUMMARY

_____

_____

_____

QUESTIONS

_____

_____

_____

_____

Personal Bible Study 2

DATE _____

SCRIPTURE PASSAGE_____

KEY IDEAS

_____

_____

_____

APPLICATION

_____

_____

_____

_____

SUMMARY

_____

_____

_____

_____

QUESTIONS

_____

_____

_____

_____

Personal Bible Study 3

DATE _____

SCRIPTURE PASSAGE_____

KEY IDEAS

_____

_____

_____

APPLICATION

_____

_____

_____

_____

SUMMARY

_____

_____

_____

_____

QUESTIONS

_____

_____

_____

_____

Personal Bible Study 4

DATE _____

SCRIPTURE PASSAGE_____

KEY IDEAS

_____

_____

_____

APPLICATION

_____

_____

_____

_____

SUMMARY

_____

_____

_____

_____

QUESTIONS

_____

_____

_____

_____

Personal Bible Study 5

DATE _____

SCRIPTURE PASSAGE_____

KEY IDEAS

_____

_____

_____

APPLICATION

_____

_____

_____

SUMMARY

_____

_____

_____

QUESTIONS

_____

_____

_____

_____

Personal Bible Study 6

DATE _____

SCRIPTURE PASSAGE_____

KEY IDEAS

_____

APPLICATION

_____

SUMMARY

_____

QUESTIONS

_____

Personal Bible Study 7

DATE _____

SCRIPTURE PASSAGE_____

KEY IDEAS

_____

APPLICATION

_____

SUMMARY

_____

QUESTIONS

_____

Group Bible Study

DATE _____

SCRIPTURE PASSAGE_____

KEY IDEAS

_____

_____

_____

APPLICATION

_____

_____

_____

_____

SUMMARY

_____

_____

_____

_____

QUESTIONS

_____

_____

_____

_____

WEEK 10

FOR THE WEEK OF _____ TO_____

MEMORY VERSE _____

_____

_____

MY PRAYER LIST

☐ _____

☐ _____

☐ _____

☐ _____

☐ _____

☐ _____

☐ _____

☐ _____

"GOD LOVES AND CARES FOR YOU.

HE WANTS YOU TO REALIZE THAT HE IS WAITING

WITH OPEN ARMS TO CARRY YOU THROUGH YOUR

MOST DIFFICULT DAYS."

–Rodney Gage

Rodney Gage, *The Relationship Revolution* (Nashville: LifeWay Press, 1999), 19.

Personal Prayer

PRAISE

I exalt You, my God the King, and praise Your name forever and ever. I will praise You every day; I will honor Your name forever and ever. The Lord is great and is highly praised; His greatness is unsearchable (Ps. 145:1-3).

_____

_____

_____

THANKSGIVING

I will give thanks to You because You have answered me and have become my salvation (Ps. 118:21).

_____

_____

_____

_____

_____

CONFESSION

Purify me with hyssop, and I will be clean; wash me, and I will be whiter than snow. . . . Turn Your face away from my sins and blot out all my guilt (Ps. 51:7,9).

_____

_____

_____

_____

Personal Bible Study 1

Date _____

Scripture Passage_____

Key Ideas

_____

_____

_____

Application

_____

_____

_____

_____

Summary

_____

_____

_____

_____

Questions

_____

_____

_____

_____

Personal Bible Study 2

DATE _____

SCRIPTURE PASSAGE_____

KEY IDEAS

_____

_____

_____

APPLICATION

_____

_____

_____

SUMMARY

_____

_____

_____

QUESTIONS

_____

_____

_____

_____

Personal Bible Study 3

DATE _____

SCRIPTURE PASSAGE _____

KEY IDEAS

_____

_____

_____

APPLICATION

_____

_____

_____

_____

SUMMARY

_____

_____

_____

_____

QUESTIONS

_____

_____

_____

_____

Personal Bible Study 4

DATE _____

SCRIPTURE PASSAGE _____

KEY IDEAS

_____

_____

_____

APPLICATION

_____

_____

_____

_____

SUMMARY

_____

_____

_____

_____

QUESTIONS

_____

_____

_____

_____

Personal Bible Study 5

DATE _____

SCRIPTURE PASSAGE _____

KEY IDEAS

_____

_____

_____

APPLICATION

_____

_____

_____

_____

SUMMARY

_____

_____

_____

_____

QUESTIONS

_____

_____

_____

_____

Personal Bible Study 6

DATE _____

SCRIPTURE PASSAGE_____

KEY IDEAS

_____

APPLICATION

_____

SUMMARY

_____

QUESTIONS

_____

Personal Bible Study 7

DATE _____

SCRIPTURE PASSAGE_____

KEY IDEAS

_____

APPLICATION

_____

SUMMARY

_____

QUESTIONS

_____

Group Bible Study

DATE _____

SCRIPTURE PASSAGE _____

KEY IDEAS

_____

_____

_____

APPLICATION

_____

_____

_____

_____

SUMMARY

_____

_____

_____

_____

QUESTIONS

_____

_____

_____

_____

WEEK 11

FOR THE WEEK OF _____ TO_____

MEMORY VERSE_____

_____

_____

MY PRAYER LIST

☐ _____

☐ _____

☐ _____

☐ _____

☐ _____

☐ _____

☐ _____

☐ _____

"IF YOU DO NOT HAVE CLEAR INSTRUCTIONS FROM GOD IN A MATTER, PRAY AND WAIT. DEPEND ON GOD'S TIMING. HIS TIMING IS ALWAYS RIGHT AND BEST."

–Henry Blackaby

Henry Blackaby, *Experiencing God, Youth Edition* (Nashville: LifeWay Press, 1994), 72.

Personal Prayer

PRAISE

Hallelujah! Praise the Lord from the heavens; praise Him in the heights. Praise Him, all His angels; praise Him, all His hosts. Praise Him, sun and moon; praise Him, all you shining stars. Praise Him, highest heavens, and you waters above the heavens (Ps. 148:1-4).

_____

_____

_____

THANKSGIVING

Thanks be to God, who gives us the victory through our Lord Jesus Christ! (1 Cor. 15:57).

_____

_____

_____

_____

CONFESSION

Do you not know that your body is a sanctuary of the Holy Spirit who is in you, whom you have from God? You are not your own, for you were bought at a price; therefore glorify God in your body (1 Cor. 6:19-20).

_____

_____

_____

Personal Bible Study 1

DATE _____

SCRIPTURE PASSAGE_____

KEY IDEAS

_____

_____

_____

APPLICATION

_____

_____

_____

SUMMARY

_____

_____

_____

_____

QUESTIONS

_____

_____

_____

_____

Personal Bible Study 2

DATE _____

SCRIPTURE PASSAGE _____

KEY IDEAS

_____

_____

_____

APPLICATION

_____

_____

_____

_____

SUMMARY

_____

_____

_____

_____

QUESTIONS

_____

_____

_____

_____

Personal Bible Study 3

DATE _____

SCRIPTURE PASSAGE_____

KEY IDEAS

_____

_____

_____

APPLICATION

_____

_____

_____

_____

SUMMARY

_____

_____

_____

_____

QUESTIONS

_____

_____

_____

_____

Personal Bible Study 4

DATE _____

SCRIPTURE PASSAGE_____

KEY IDEAS

_____

_____

_____

APPLICATION

_____

_____

_____

_____

SUMMARY

_____

_____

_____

_____

QUESTIONS

_____

_____

_____

_____

Personal Bible Study 5

DATE _____

SCRIPTURE PASSAGE_____

KEY IDEAS

_____

_____

_____

APPLICATION

_____

_____

_____

_____

SUMMARY

_____

_____

_____

_____

QUESTIONS

_____

_____

_____

_____

Personal Bible Study 6

DATE _____

SCRIPTURE PASSAGE_____

KEY IDEAS

_____

APPLICATION

_____

SUMMARY

_____

QUESTIONS

_____

Personal Bible Study 7

DATE _____

SCRIPTURE PASSAGE_____

KEY IDEAS

_____

APPLICATION

_____

SUMMARY

_____

QUESTIONS

_____

Group Bible Study

DATE _____

SCRIPTURE PASSAGE_____

KEY IDEAS

_____

_____

_____

APPLICATION

_____

_____

_____

_____

SUMMARY

_____

_____

_____

_____

QUESTIONS

_____

_____

_____

_____

WEEK 1

FOR THE WEEK OF _____ TO_____

MEMORY VERSE _____

_____

_____

MY PRAYER LIST

☐ _____
☐ _____
☐ _____
☐ _____
☐ _____
☐ _____
☐ _____
☐ _____

"IF A SUPERIOR GOD CREATED US FOR A PURPOSE,

THEN THE MOST LOGICAL APPROACH IS TO ASK,

WHAT IS THAT PURPOSE AND HOW DO WE LIVE TO

FULFILL IT? THE ANSWER IS FOUND IN GOD'S WORD."

–Charles Colson

Charles Colson, *How Now Shall We Live? Student Edition* (Nashville: LifeWay Press, 2000), 64.

Personal Prayer

PRAISE

Hallelujah! Sing to the Lord a new song, His praise in the assembly of the godly. . . . For the Lord takes pleasure in His people; He adorns the humble with salvation (Ps.149:1,4).

_____

_____

_____

THANKSGIVING

Devote yourselves to prayer; stay alert in it with thanksgiving (Col. 4:2).

_____

_____

_____

_____

CONFESSION

No one undergoing a trial should say, "I am being tempted by God." For God is not tempted by evil, and He Himself doesn't tempt anyone. But each person is tempted when he is drawn away and enticed by his own evil desires. Then after desire has conceived, it gives birth to sin, and when sin is fully grown, it gives birth to death (Jas. 1:13-15).

_____

_____

_____

Personal Bible Study 1

DATE _____

SCRIPTURE PASSAGE_____

KEY IDEAS

_____

_____

_____

APPLICATION

_____

_____

_____

SUMMARY

_____

_____

_____

QUESTIONS

_____

_____

_____

Personal Bible Study 2

DATE _____

SCRIPTURE PASSAGE_____

KEY IDEAS

_____

_____

_____

APPLICATION

_____

_____

_____

SUMMARY

_____

_____

_____

QUESTIONS

_____

_____

_____

_____

Personal Bible Study 3

DATE _____

SCRIPTURE PASSAGE_____

KEY IDEAS

_____

_____

_____

APPLICATION

_____

_____

_____

_____

SUMMARY

_____

_____

_____

_____

QUESTIONS

_____

_____

_____

_____

Personal Bible Study 4

DATE _____

SCRIPTURE PASSAGE_____

KEY IDEAS

_____

_____

_____

APPLICATION

_____

_____

_____

SUMMARY

_____

_____

_____

QUESTIONS

_____

_____

_____

_____

Personal Bible Study 5

DATE _____

SCRIPTURE PASSAGE_____

KEY IDEAS

_____

_____

_____

APPLICATION

_____

_____

_____

_____

SUMMARY

_____

_____

_____

_____

QUESTIONS

_____

_____

_____

_____

Personal Bible Study 6

DATE _____

SCRIPTURE PASSAGE_____

KEY IDEAS

_____

APPLICATION

_____

SUMMARY

_____

QUESTIONS

_____

Personal Bible Study 7

DATE _____

SCRIPTURE PASSAGE_____

KEY IDEAS

_____

APPLICATION

_____

SUMMARY

_____

QUESTIONS

_____

Group Bible Study

DATE _____

SCRIPTURE PASSAGE_____

KEY IDEAS

_____

_____

_____

APPLICATION

_____

_____

_____

_____

SUMMARY

_____

_____

_____

_____

QUESTIONS

_____

_____

_____

_____

WEEK 13

FOR THE WEEK OF _____ TO_____

MEMORY VERSE _____

_____

_____

MY PRAYER LIST

☐ _____

☐ _____

☐ _____

☐ _____

☐ _____

☐ _____

☐ _____

☐ _____

"WHICH BRINGS ME BACK TO ADAM AND EVE.
WHAT WERE THEY DOING JUST HANGING AROUND THAT TREE?
GIVEN A GARDEN OF DELIGHT, OF ENDLESS INDULGENCE,
WHY DID THEY CHOOSE TO HANG AROUND THE ONE
TREE THAT WAS FORBIDDEN?"

–Erwin Raphael McManus

Erwin Raphael McManus, *Uprising: A Revolution of the Soul* (Nashville: Thomas Nelson Publishers, 2003), 14.

Personal Prayer

PRAISE

Hallelujah! Praise God in His sanctuary. Praise Him in His mighty heavens. Praise Him for His powerful acts; praise Him for His abundant greatness (Ps. 150:1-2).

_____

_____

_____

THANKSGIVING

For everything created by God is good, and nothing should be rejected if it is received with thanksgiving (1 Tim. 4:4).

_____

_____

_____

_____

_____

CONFESSION

God, create a clean heart for me and renew a steadfast spirit within me. Do not banish me from Your presence or take Your Holy Spirit from me. Restore the joy of Your salvation to me, and give me a willing spirit (Ps. 51:10-12).

_____

_____

_____

_____

Personal Bible Study 1

DATE _____

SCRIPTURE PASSAGE_____

KEY IDEAS

_____

_____

_____

APPLICATION

_____

_____

_____

_____

SUMMARY

_____

_____

_____

_____

QUESTIONS

_____

_____

_____

_____

Personal Bible Study 2

DATE _____

SCRIPTURE PASSAGE_____

KEY IDEAS

_____

_____

_____

APPLICATION

_____

_____

_____

_____

SUMMARY

_____

_____

_____

_____

QUESTIONS

_____

_____

_____

_____

Personal Bible Study 3

DATE _____

SCRIPTURE PASSAGE_____

KEY IDEAS

_____

_____

_____

APPLICATION

_____

_____

_____

_____

SUMMARY

_____

_____

_____

_____

QUESTIONS

_____

_____

_____

Personal Bible Study 4

DATE _____

SCRIPTURE PASSAGE _____

KEY IDEAS

_____

_____

_____

APPLICATION

_____

_____

_____

_____

SUMMARY

_____

_____

_____

_____

QUESTIONS

_____

_____

_____

_____

Personal Bible Study 5

DATE _____

SCRIPTURE PASSAGE_____

KEY IDEAS

_____

_____

_____

APPLICATION

_____

_____

_____

SUMMARY

_____

_____

_____

_____

QUESTIONS

_____

_____

_____

_____

Verses to Memorize

Make a list of verses you would like to memorize. Here are some suggested verses that deal with specific issues.

- ☐ **Anger** Ephesians 4:26
- ☐ **Arguments** Titus 3:9
- ☐ **Broken Relationships**
  Matthew 5:23-24
- ☐ **Cheating** Proverbs 20:17
- ☐ **Compromise** Daniel 1:8
- ☐ **Dishonesty** Psalm 34:13
- ☐ **God's Creation** Psalm 24:1-2
- ☐ **Confronting** Galatians 6:1
- ☐ **Witnessing** Romans 1:16
- ☐ **Worship** 1 Chronicles 16:29
- ☐ **Fighting** Proverbs 17:14
- ☐ **Gossiping** Proverbs 16:28
- ☐ **Homosexuality**
  1 Corinthians 6:9-11
- ☐ **Hurtful Language** Ephesians 4:29
- ☐ **Hurting Self** 1 Corinthians 6:19-20
- ☐ **Laziness** Proverbs 6:9-11
- ☐ **Lust** 1 Thessalonians 4:3-5
- ☐ **Bad Influences** 1 Corinthians 15:33
- ☐ **Neglecting Church** Hebrews 10:25
- ☐ **Neglecting Scripture**
  2 Timothy 3:14-15
- ☐ **Off-color Humor** Ephesians 5:3-4
- ☐ **Causing Harm** Proverbs 24:1-2
- ☐ **Pornography** Job 31:1
- ☐ **Prayerlessness** Mark 14:38
- ☐ **Prejudice** Galatians 3:26-28
- ☐ **Profanity** 1 Timothy 4:12
- ☐ **Rage** Colossians 3:8
- ☐ **Rebellion** Romans 13:1-2
- ☐ **Resentment** Colossians 3:13
- ☐ **Secret Sins** James 5:16
- ☐ **Selfishness** Philippians 2:3
- ☐ **Premarital Sex** 1 Corinthians 6:18

- ☐ **Stealing** Ephesians 4:28
- ☐ **Use of Alcohol** Proverbs 20:1
- ☐ **Violence** Proverbs 11:17
- ☐ _____
- ☐ _____
- ☐ _____
- ☐ _____
- ☐ _____
- ☐ _____
- ☐ _____
- ☐ _____
- ☐ _____
- ☐ _____
- ☐ _____
- ☐ _____
- ☐ _____
- ☐ _____
- ☐ _____
- ☐ _____
- ☐ _____
- ☐ _____
- ☐ _____
- ☐ _____
- ☐ _____
- ☐ _____
- ☐ _____
- ☐ _____
- ☐ _____
- ☐ _____
- ☐ _____
- ☐ _____
- ☐ _____
- ☐ _____
- ☐ _____

Bible Reading Record

Keep track of Scripture reading by marking an *X* over the number each time you read a chapter.

OLD TESTAMENT

Genesis 1 2 3 4 5 6 7 8 9 10 11 12 13 14 15 16 17 18 19 20 21 22 23 24 25 26 27 28 29 30 31 32 33 34 35 36 37 38 39 40 41 42 43 44 45 46 47 48 49 50
Exodus 1 2 3 4 5 6 7 8 9 10 11 12 13 14 15 16 17 18 19 20 21 22 23 24 25 26 27 28 29 30 31 32 33 34 35 36 37 38 39 40
Leviticus 1 2 3 4 5 6 7 8 9 10 11 12 13 14 15 16 17 18 19 20 21 22 23 24 25 26 27
Numbers 1 2 3 4 5 6 7 8 9 10 11 12 13 14 15 16 17 18 19 20 21 22 23 24 25 26 27 28 29 30 31 32 33 34 35 36
Deuteronomy 1 2 3 4 5 6 7 8 9 10 11 12 13 14 15 16 17 18 19 20 21 22 23 24 25 26 27 28 29 30 31 32 33 34
Joshua 1 2 3 4 5 6 7 8 9 10 11 12 13 14 15 16 17 18 19 20 21 22 23 24
Judges 1 2 3 4 5 6 7 8 9 10 11 12 13 14 15 16 17 18 19 20 21
Ruth 1 2 3 4
1 Samuel 1 2 3 4 5 6 7 8 9 10 11 12 13 14 15 16 17 18 19 20 21 22 23 24 25 26 27 28 29 30 31
2 Samuel 1 2 3 4 5 6 7 8 9 10 11 12 13 14 15 16 17 18 19 20 21 22 23 24
1 Kings 1 2 3 4 5 6 7 8 9 10 11 12 13 14 15 16 17 18 19 20 21 22
2 Kings 1 2 3 4 5 6 7 8 9 10 11 12 13 14 15 16 17 18 19 20 21 22 23 24 25
1 Chronicles 1 2 3 4 5 6 7 8 9 10 11 12 13 14 15 16 17 18 19 20 21 22 23 24 25 26 27 28 29
2 Chronicles 1 2 3 4 5 6 7 8 9 10 11 12 13 14 15 16 17 18 19 20 21 22 23 24 25 26 27 28 29 30 31 32 33 34 35 36
Ezra 1 2 3 4 5 6 7 8 9 10
Nehemiah 1 2 3 4 5 6 7 8 9 10 11 12 13
Esther 1 2 3 4 5 6 7 8 9 10
Job 1 2 3 4 5 6 7 8 9 10 11 12 13 14 15 16 17 18 19 20 21 22 23 24 25 26 27 28 29 30 31 32 33 34 35 36 37 38 39 40 41 42
Psalms 1 2 3 4 5 6 7 8 9 10 11 12 13 14 15 16 17 18 19 20 21 22 23 24 25 26 27 28 29 30 31 32 33 34 35 36 37 38 39 40 41 42 43 44 45 46 47 48 49 50 51 52 53 54 55 56 57 58 59 60 61 62 63 64 65 66 67 68 69 70 71 72 73 74 75 76 77 78 79 80 81 82 83 84 85 86 87 88 89 90 91 92 93 94 95 96 97 98 99 100 101 102 103 104 105 106 107 108 109 110 111 112 113 114 115 116 117 118 119 120 121 122 123 124 125 126 127 128 129 130 131 132 133 134 135 136 137 138 139 140 141 142 143 144 145 146 147 148 149 150
Proverbs 1 2 3 4 5 6 7 8 9 10 11 12 13 14 15 16 17 18 19 20 21 22 23 24 25 26 27 28 29 30 31
Ecclesiastes 1 2 3 4 5 6 7 8 9 10 11 12
Song of Songs 1 2 3 4 5 6 7 8
Isaiah 1 2 3 4 5 6 7 8 9 10 11 12 13 14 15 16 17 18 19 20 21 22 23 24 25 26 27 28 29 30 31 32 33 34 35 36 37 38 39 40 41 42 43 44 45 46 47 48 49 50 51 52 53 54 55 56 57 58 59 60 61 62 63 64 65 66

Jeremiah 1 2 3 4 5 6 7 8 9 10 11 12 13 14 15 16 17 18 19 20 21 22 23 24 25 26 27 28 29 30 31 32 33 34 35 36 37 38 39 40 41 42 43 44 45 46 47 48 49 50 51 52
Lamentations 1 2 3 4 5
Ezekiel 1 2 3 4 5 6 7 8 9 10 11 12 13 14 15 16 17 18 19 20 21 22 23 24 25 26 27 28 29 30 31 32 33 34 35 36 37 38 39 40 41 42 43 44 45 46 47 48
Daniel 1 2 3 4 5 6 7 8 9 10 11 12
Hosea 1 2 3 4 5 6 7 8 9 10 11 12 13 14
Joel 1 2 3
Amos 1 2 3 4 5 6 7 8 9
Obadiah 1
Jonah 1 2 3 4
Micah 1 2 3 4 5 6 7
Nahum 1 2 3
Habakkuk 1 2 3
Zephaniah 1 2 3
Haggai 1 2
Zechariah 1 2 3 4 5 6 7 8 9 10 11 12 13 14
Malachi 1 2 3 4

NEW TESTAMENT

Matthew 1 2 3 4 5 6 7 8 9 10 11 12 13 14 15 16 17 18 19 20 21 22 23 24 25 26 27 28
Mark 1 2 3 4 5 6 7 8 9 10 11 12 13 14 15 16
Luke 1 2 3 4 5 6 7 8 9 10 11 12 13 14 15 16 17 18 19 20 21 22 23 24
John 1 2 3 4 5 6 7 8 9 10 11 12 13 14 15 16 17 18 19 20 21
Acts 1 2 3 4 5 6 7 8 9 10 11 12 13 14 15 16 17 18 19 20 21 22 23 24 25 26 27 28
Romans 1 2 3 4 5 6 7 8 9 10 11 12 13 14 15 16
1 Corinthians 1 2 3 4 5 6 7 8 9 10 11 12 13 14 15 16
2 Corinthians 1 2 3 4 5 6 7 8 9 10 11 12 13
Galatians 1 2 3 4 5 6
Ephesians 1 2 3 4 5 6
Philippians 1 2 3 4
Colossians 1 2 3 4
1 Thessalonians 1 2 3 4 5
2 Thessalonians 1 2 3
1 Timothy 1 2 3 4 5 6
2 Timothy 1 2 3 4
Titus 1 2 3
Philemon 1
Hebrews 1 2 3 4 5 6 7 8 9 10 11 12 13
James 1 2 3 4 5
1 Peter 1 2 3 4 5
2 Peter 1 2 3
1 John 1 2 3 4 5
2 John 1
3 John 1
Jude 1
Revelation 1 2 3 4 5 6 7 8 9 10 11 12 13 14 15 16 17 18 19 20 21 22